The My

Who Sabotaged Ar

On 9th May 1812, Bristol's me
and businessmen gathered in Queen Square to witness
an event which was hailed as 'a new dawn of transport
and travel' and one which offered a potentially massive
investment opportunity. After a lifetime of experiments
and research, local inventor Archie Russell claimed to
have perfected the art of hot air balloon technology,
with a machine which promised to fly higher, faster,
and further than ever before.

On the day of the test flight, weather
conditions were perfect and
spectators and reporters waited in
anticipation for a glimpse of this
revolutionary new machine. However
as Archie's balloon began to lift off
from behind a concealed curtain, the
crowd gasped as it veered violently
and crashed into a tree below.

On further inspection Archie noticed that someone had
got to his precious balloon moments before take-off and
cut one of his essential steering ropes in a terrible act of
sabotage! Why would someone want to destroy Archie's
life's work? Was it a personal grudge against him? Or
did a competitor want to stifle the competition? Retrace
the suspects' footsteps, solve the clues, and finally
uncover the truth of this legendary Bristol mystery!

*The story of the Sabotaged Balloon detailed throughout this
book is fictional, however the historical information and all
extra details related to each clue is factual and based on
detailed historical research.*

HOW TO PLAY

1 Follow the Maps
to find the location
of your clue

2 Solve the Clue to eliminate one
option from the list on page 1
(Extra help is on the back page)

3 At each stop you will
Unravel more of
the legendary tale.

4 At the end of your adventure your last
remaining items on Page 1 will
Reveal the final Secrets of the Mystery

IMPORTANT INFORMATION

1 On rare occasions, clues may be temporarily covered or permanently removed. In this instance we ask you to use the extra clues at the back the book, and if possible, please report this to us.
It is recommended that you do the activity within 3 months of purchase, to reduce this risk.

2 Take care! You are responsible for yourself and your group. Be careful crossing roads, make sure to respect old monuments and private property, and if you are drinking alcohol please drink responsibly.

3 Any food & drink discounts available in this booklet are at the discretio of the stated premises, and may be subject to change or cancellation.

DIRECTIONS TO STARTING POINT

THE STARTING POINT FOR THIS ADVENTURE IS:

BRISTOL OLD VIC, KING ST, BRISTOL BS1 4ED

ONCE ARRIVING AT THE STARTING POINT, YOUR MYSTERY ADVENTURE CAN BEGIN!

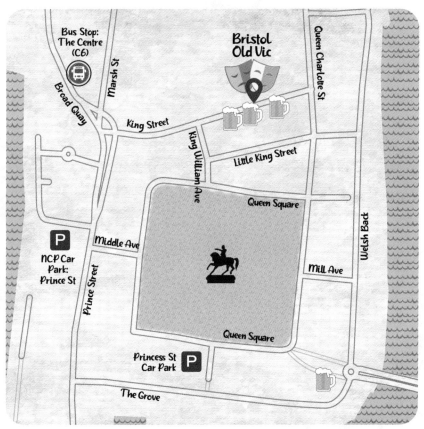

Cooper's Hall

Bristol has a long association with hot air balloons; a craze which started way back in 1784 when Michael Biaggini held a 3-day exhibition inside Cooper's Hall (the grand building in front of you, now part of the Old Vic). Visitors paid 2 shillings 6p for a glimpse of the astonishing new invention and marvelled when the 30-foot balloon was inflated inside the hall.

Hot air ballooning was in fact invented in France one year earlier, by the Montgolfier brothers, who showcased their invention in front of King Louis XVI and Marie Antoinette with a sheep, duck and cockerel as the first ever flight passengers. The King was so impressed he named the animals 'heroes of the air' and gave them a special place inside his menagerie at his palace of Versailles.

Clue 1

Find a meeting time hidden in this poem:

(No need to search for anything at the location)

Many have toiled and bravely fought,

In vain to reach the skies,

Did the plight of Icarus not warn of your demise?

Now in this message you will find

In time for your next clue,

Getting started <u>from the top</u> it's <u>placed in front</u> of you.

Heroes of the big balloons were famous in this town,

Though flying high on the up, must one day <u>come down</u>

(Extra help on back page)

Eliminate a meeting time

Story

The Cooper's Hall hot air balloon exhibition of 1784 was a life-changing moment for little Archie Russell, who at the age of ten was lucky enough to attend the show with his father who had been given two tickets by a regular customer of his cobblers shop.

Dumbstruck by the remarkable sight of such an amazing invention, Archie swore at that moment that he would devote his life to the science of flight, and vowed to create 'the greatest flying machine that the world had ever seen'.

Although hailing from a humble background, Archie's father was supportive of his son's passion, and sent him to the best schools that he could afford. Archie returned the favour with outstanding exam results.

Directions

As you face the Old Vic theatre, turn right and head along King Street until you reach Queen Charlotte Street.

Turn left, and continue until you get to Baldwin Street, then turn right. Cross at the first set of traffic lights, and take the steps leading up to St Nicholas Street, then turn right. Your next clue can be found on the short stretch of St Nicholas Street in front of you.

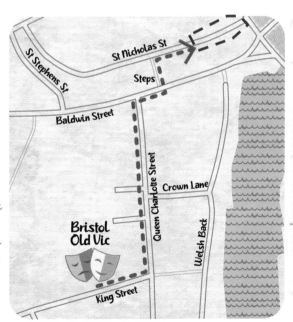

6

St Nicholas Market

You are now outside St Nicholas Market, home to the mos
famous clock in Bristol which peculiarly has two separate minut
hands. Prior to the widespread use of GMT, time was kept b
observing the sunrise and ringing church bells, which made Brist
11 minutes behind London. To keep local tradition, when th
Great Western Railway came into use in 1841, the Brist
Corporation installed a clock which kept both London and Brist
time, causing huge confusion to passengers.
In 1884 Greenwich Mean Time won a vote held at a
international conference in Washington DC to become the glob
Prime Meridian for international use. France, favouring a mor
neutral name, abstained on the vote and continued using 'Par
Time' until 1911.

Clue 2

You need to find something in this
short stretch of St Nicholas Street
(don't enter the market)

About your suspects it was said,

spent nights in bars and days in bed.

An alternative was given instead,

to _drinking at the Old Queen's Head._

ELIMINATE

Eliminate a suspect

Story

Although excelling in education, Archie lacked the resources or funds for the kind of investment he needed to work on such an expensive machine.

At the age of 18 he began selling scientific books and equipment as well as magic tricks at St Nicholas Market and gradually saved enough money for a small workshop nearby. During this time Archie was able to produce an amazing model prototype and seemed to be making huge progress in his dream to create a manned flying machine.

However, times were hard and several economic crashes as well as constant national war pushed up the price of raw materials and made his enterprise unsustainable, forcing him to give up his workshop.

Directions

A small alley named All Saints Lane will take you through St Nicholas Market (the old clock is on your left as you emerge onto Corn Street). To continue on your route, head in the opposite direction along Corn Street, then as you pass through the black bollards, turn left into Broad Street.

Your next clue can be found somewhere on this street.

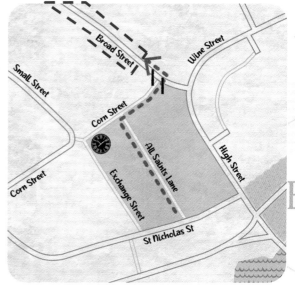

Broad Street

Clue 3

Search high on Broad Street for three round metal plaques. The words on these plaques will help you complete the rhyme below:

In case of nasty ____2____ you'd want to keep one close, for ___1___ can be the end of __3__, and what you value most.

Eliminate a tavern

Story

Financially broke, Archie was forced to take a job in a local insurance company, where he stayed until he was 34. Whilst not making progress on his balloon, it was while working here that Archie devised a way to attract investment for his revolutionary invention.

Bristol's treacherous inland tidal harbour was often a cause of shipwrecks, and its surrounding road network was plagued with highwaymen; which drove up insurance premiums and made travel expensive. An air balloon could bypass the dangerous roads and avoid the time restrictions of Bristol's tidal harbour! It was his eureka moment and set a plan in motion to secure investment.

Before the Great Fire of London in 1666, there was no organised fire service, and with most structures built of wood, outbreaks were common. In response to the tragedy, the 'Fire Office' was established, and private insurance companies were set up to provide a service for those who could afford to pay their premiums. A badge / fire mark was provided to policy holders, who could display it on the outside of their home as indication of their cover. Unfortunately buildings were often left to burn as the right company was found to deal with the right building. An example of an early fire badge can still be found at the bottom of the Christmas Steps (the location of your 5th clue) and is marked on the map to that clue.

Directions

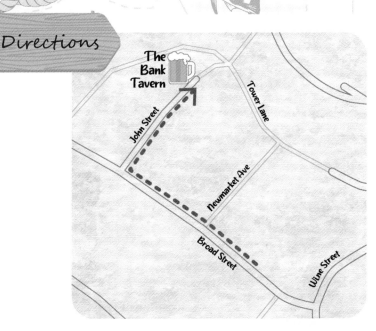

Continue along Broad Street until you see a small alley on your right called John Street. At the end of this alley is The Bank Tavern, your first optional pub stop.

The private banking industry boomed in Bristol due to the presence of a large number of wealthy merchants, however in 1825 a huge economic bubble burst, causing widespread financial misery and bankruptcy to the city. Large investments in post-war Britain were causing prices to skyrocket and tempted people to make bolder and riskier investments. An infamous fraudster named General Gregor Macgregor took advantage of the situation, and invented a fictional South American territory named 'Poyais' and encouraged people to invest millions in government bonds and land certificates for a place that did not exist. This fraudulent scheme was a major factor in the crash of 1825 and gained Macgregor the reputation of 'the most 'brazen confidence trickster in history'.

Clue 4

(You don't need to find anything at the location to solve this clue)

5 =

_____ S_

4 =

_____ S_

6 =

_____ S_

3 =

_____ S_

Identify the relevant objects, and then take the underlined letters in red to make a 4-letter word which is related to the name of a tavern

ELIMINATE

Eliminate a tavern

Story

Archie's new quest to raise funds started at the bank, where he hoped to secure a loan to start the ball rolling and promote his idea to investors.

While reluctant to lend him money due to his financial history, the bank agreed to accept Archie's home as a security deposit and lent him most of the money he needed to get started. Hiding this risky financial strategy from his wife, Archie began to visit coffee houses & local taverns that were frequented by wealthy businessmen in the hope of drumming up interest in his idea. It was while drinking in this tavern that Archie met a successful insurance broker, who was extremely interested in his idea and wanted to be involved.

Directions

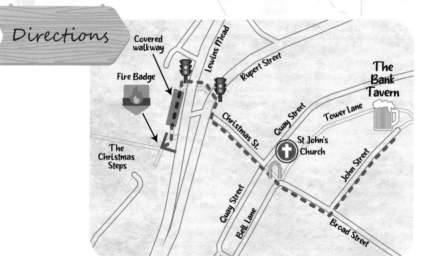

Exit the Bank Tavern and re-join Broad Street. Turn right and head through the old gate under the clock tower. Continue straight across the road onto Christmas Street, and keep walking until you reach 2 traffic light crossings. After crossing the road, on your left you will see a covered walkway. Head through this, and as you emerge you will see a set of old timbered buildings on your right. This is the bottom of the Christmas Steps. See if you can spot the old fire badge on the white corner building. **12**

Christmas Steps

Before these steps were completed in 1669, this would have been a steep, slippery and perilous dirt track. Such conditions made it a perfect spot for muggers, who would hide in the shadows and purposely trip unsuspecting folk down the hill, before robbing them of their possessions.

At the top of the steps you will see a very small chapel, which is devoted to the Three Wise Men and has stained glass windows depicting the nativity of Jesus. This is one of the theories as to why the steps bear their unusual name.

Clue 5

Find this plaque on the Christmas Step

THIS STREETE WAS STEPPERED (6) & FINISHED SEPTEMBER 1669. THE RIGHT WORPFL THOMAS ST(1)S ESQR THEN MAYOR. HUMPHRY (3) AND (9)ARD H(11). SHERRIFFES THE RIGHT WORPFL ROBERT YEAMNS KNT. & BARRONET MAYOR ELECT. CHARLES POWELL AND EDWARD HORNE SHERRIFFE ELECT OF THIS CITY. (10) (8) AT THE (4) OF JON-ATHAN BLACK(7) ESQR FORMERELY SHERRIFFE OF THIS CITTY AND (2)WARDS ALDER(5) OF THE CITY OF LONDON & BY YE SAID SIR ROBERT YEAMAN. WHEN MAYOR AND ALDERMAN OF THIS CITY NAMED QUEENE STREETE.

Arrange the missing words in numerical order to eliminate a business

ELIMINATE

Story

In 1810 Archie had enough investment and enthusiasm for his idea that he quit his job and spent his time developing a full-sized flying machine based on the miniature models he had made in his workshop. By 1812 a working prototype had been produced and he was ready to showcase his radical new design to the world. In an attempt to replicate the amazing success of Biaggini's 1784 indoor exhibition that he had attended as a child, Archie wanted to book Cooper's Hall as the venue for his unveiling. Archie enticed the theatre owner by offering him 100% of the ticket revenue which persuaded him to cancel an art auction he had already scheduled for May.

Directions

As you emerge from the Christmas Steps turn left, and head along Colston Street, keeping the old Almshouses on your left.

As the road splits, follow it right and uphill along Trenchard Street. After around 200M you will see the Hatchet Inn.

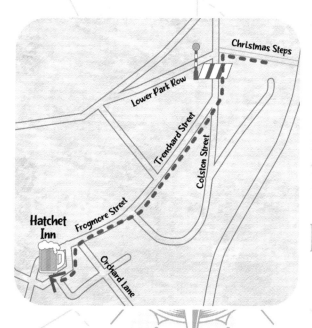

The Hatchet

The Hatchet Inn is Bristol's oldest and arguably most famous establishment, with a notoriously gruesome past. As well as being home to a bare-knuckle boxing ring, dog-fighting & cock -fighting pit, if you believe the story, its front door is said to be lined with the skin of an executed criminal.

Legend has it that Edward Teach, also known as the fearsome 'Blackbeard' was a patron of this pub, having been born in the Redcliffe area around 1680. With lit fuses in his hair to give him a demonic appearance, Blackbeard captured and looted 23 ships around the Caribbean in his lifetime, from his stolen flagship 'Queen Anne's Revenge'. It took five gunshot wounds and twenty sword cuts to finally kill the famous captain, after which, his head was cut off so that the victors could secure a bounty. Legend has it that after his headless body was thrown overboard, it swam around the ship three times.

Clue 6

Find a triangular plaque on the outside of the pub, and translate the symbols to letters to decode the message below:

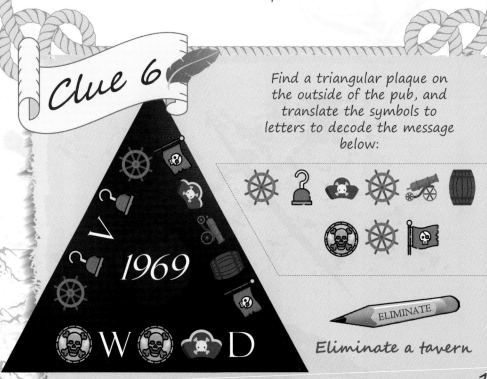

ELIMINATE

Eliminate a tavern

Story

It was while drinking in this pub one night that Archie had a chance encounter with a local cheese-maker who was quickly making a name for herself as a talented businesswoman. She proposed the innovative idea of creating a celebratory balloon-shaped cheese that she could sell in the city in the lead up to the event called 'The Archie Blue'. Not only did the idea capture the mind of Archie, but if you believe the rumours, she also captured his heart. In the months leading up to the exhibition the two of them became inseparable and tongues were wagging about the nature of their relationship. After all, the cheesemaker was married to a well-known local newspaper owner, and Archie himself had a loving wife.

Directions

Exit the Hatchet Inn from its gruesome door, and head south along Denmark Avenue. Take the first right onto Unity Street, and continue straight towards the large brick arch in front of you.

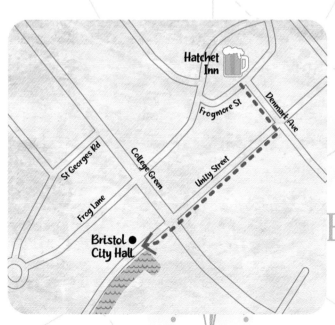

16

Bristol City Hall

Due to the city's rich maritime trade, a host of industries popped up in Bristol which specialised in the refining of raw material imported from the New World such as sugar, tobacco, and cocoa. Joseph Fry was an example of an industrious local who specialised in the refinement of cocoa, and after acquiring a small shop along with a mechanical patent, founded Fry's Chocolate Factory in 1761. Fry's factory went on to create the world's first mass produced chocolate bar in 1847, and the world's first ever chocolate Easter egg in 1873.

Clue 7

Find seven letters that appear after the name 'Frank Sheppard' on a nearby plaque. Place the left-hand chocolate pieces in order according to those letters, and use the right-hand pieces to spell out a message. **Eliminate a business.**

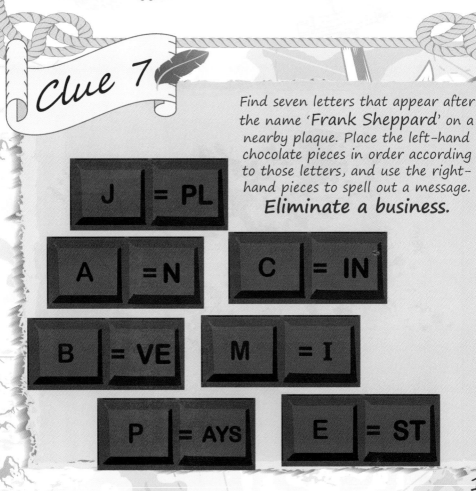

J = PL

A = N

C = IN

B = VE

M = I

P = AYS

E = ST

Story

Just one month before the indoor exhibition was due to take place at Cooper's Hall, the cheesemaker persuaded Archie that if he wanted to capture the imagination of the city and investors alike, he needed to showcase his invention outside, and conduct a live maiden flight. Only then could people be excited by ballooning again and see the real potential of his invention.

Agreeing with this decision, Archie made the bold move of cancelling the planned exhibition at Cooper's Hall, leading to huge financial loss for the theatre owner and upsetting the art investor who had already lost the slot for his auction due to Archie's booking.

Directions

Follow the path into the park, keeping the water on your right-hand side.

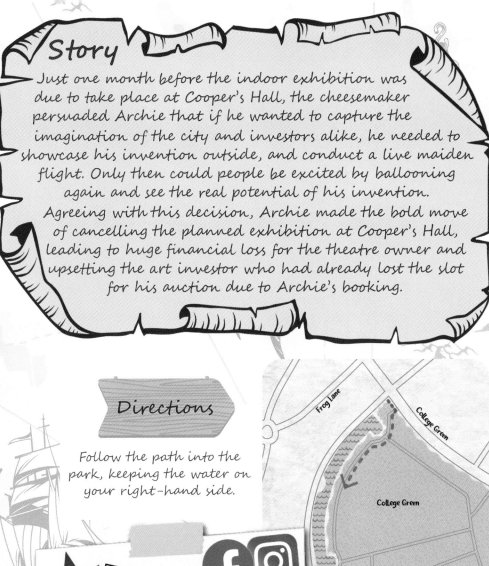

Frog Lane

College Green

College Green

PHOTO STOP!

Take a photo

Tag on social media: @mysteryguides

For a chance to win a prize!!

18

Merchant Traders

In 1720 the people of Bristol, like the rest of the country, experienced the most famous financial crash in history, known as the South Sea Bubble. Investors and speculators were confident that following the War of the Spanish Succession, Britain would secure lucrative contracts to deal in slaves with territories in South America, with King George himself appointed as governor of the South Sea trading company. However, terms of the deal were not what investors expected they would be, and the share price quickly plummeted. Investors lost the modern equivalent of millions, including Sir Isaac Newton, who famously stated that he 'could calculate the motions of heavenly stars but not the madness of people'.

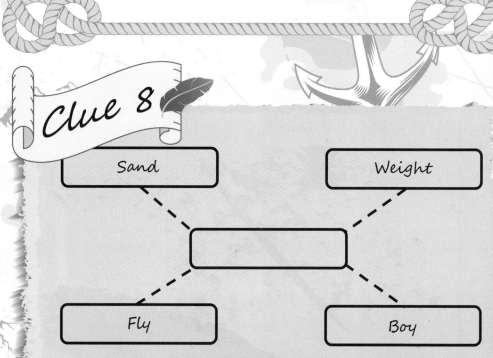

Clue 8

Sand	Weight
Fly	Boy

Find the word that links the four together. If you get stuck, look at the statue standing outside the Bristol City Council buildings and find this in his hand.

ELIMINATE

Eliminate a business associated with the word

19

Story

Through a combination of cash bribes and company shares, it was agreed with the local mayor that a stage could be constructed in Queen Square, to be used as a launching pad for Archie's special balloon.

In order for the event to be a success, it had to attract the wealthiest and most influential local businessmen, who Archie relied on to literally float the project. In order to attract such people, Archie turned to his trusted insurance-broker friend to use his vast list of contacts. A wide variety of VIPs were confirmed from the world of insurance, shipping, logistics, travel, and media, all of whom could see huge economic potential in Archie's machine if it could fly the speed and distances that he said it could.

Directions

Follow the water around to the end and then turn left, keeping Bristol Cathedral on your right hand side. Follow the path across College Green and continue straight along the cobbled street.

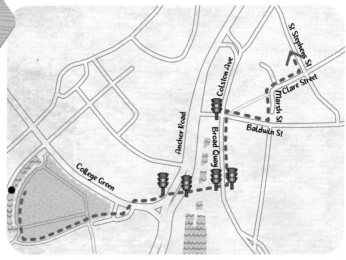

Continue straight and cross the traffic lights, until you emerge into a large open paved area. Head to the far side towards a tall glass building, and then turn left. Take the first right onto Baldwin St, then first left onto Marsh St (through the bollards). As the road bends follow it into Clare St, then take a first left into St Stephen's St. Your next clue can be found on this stretch of street.,

Clue 9

You need to search for something on this stretch of St Stephen's Street...

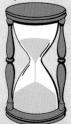 

These two objects will guide you to your next meeting time to eliminate.

Story

Two days before launch day, Bristol's largest newspaper ran a full-page front cover story exposing details of the scandalous affair between Archie and the cheesemaker, which threatened to cause huge reputational damage. How could investors trust the man who had been caught cheating on his devoted wife?

Lurid details and gossip swept across town, and VIPs started to withdraw their invitations. There was even talk of cancelling the event all together.

Rumours then turned to the finances behind the project, speculating that it was in fact another financial confidence trick to swindle wealthy investors out of their money.

The English Civil War in the mid 17th century created an increased demand for news and up-to-date information, and saw the circulation of print spread dramatically. However at this time printing was strictly controlled by the authorities and was largely inaccessible to ordinary people. All this changed in the 1690s due to a parliamentary admin error, that meant that the Licensing Act was not renewed; opening the door to an explosion of printed publications and ushering in the 'Age of Satire'. Gossip pamphlets and satirical cartoons became a common feature of the Georgian period, all thanks to this bureaucratic oversight.

Directions

Walk to the end of St Stephen's Street, and follow the road round to the right. Take the first right into Small Street.

Continue along Small Street until you see a large old building offset on your left. Look for seven shields above the door on the far left to solve your next clue.

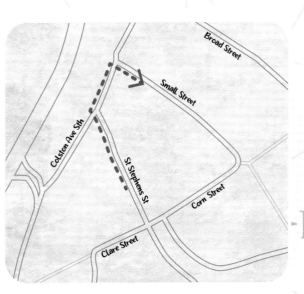

Small Street

The shield on the far left above the door is the coat of arms of Richard Amerike, who was the King's Customs Officer and main financer of John Cabot's maiden journey to the New World in 1497. He even provided the wood to build Cabot's ship from the oak trees on his private estate. A theory put forward by historian Rodney Broome, is that the newly discovered continent was named 'America' in his honour, opposing the traditional idea that it was named after Italian explorer Amerigo Vespucci.

Clue 10

Assign a shield to a letter using the 3-letter words above, then use it to decipher the 7 shields above the door of the building to eliminate a suspect.

ELIMINATE

Story

In an attempt to separate himself from the rumours of his affair, Archie broke all contact with the cheesemaker, and denied any wrongdoing had taken place. To go even further, he denied the cheesemaker use of his brand name in the marketing of her specially made balloon-shaped cheese, and cancelled her stall at Queen Square. This caused huge financial loss as thousands of cheeses had already been set and were ready to go on sale.

The dispute raged for two days and the cheesemaker even made her way into the Queen Square event and was caught close to the balloon before the launch. This appearance made her one of the key suspects in the later investigations, and the first in line for questioning.

Directions

Continue along Small Street to the end, as it bends into Corn Street.

On your right you will see a grand columned building which is The Commercial Rooms. Your next clue can be found in the back room of this pub.

If you can't enter the building, turn to the back page for help.

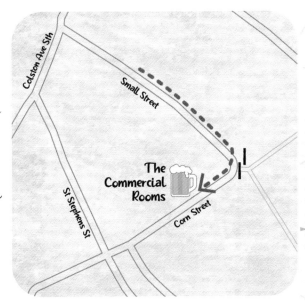

Commercial Rooms

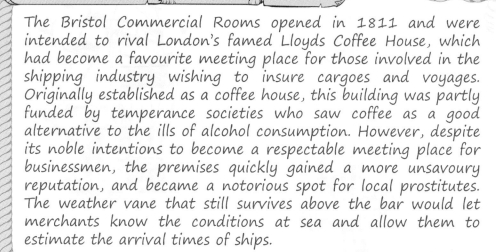

The Bristol Commercial Rooms opened in 1811 and were intended to rival London's famed Lloyds Coffee House, which had become a favourite meeting place for those involved in the shipping industry wishing to insure cargoes and voyages. Originally established as a coffee house, this building was partly funded by temperance societies who saw coffee as a good alternative to the ills of alcohol consumption. However, despite its noble intentions to become a respectable meeting place for businessmen, the premises quickly gained a more unsavoury reputation, and became a notorious spot for local prostitutes. The weather vane that still survives above the bar would let merchants know the conditions at sea and allow them to estimate the arrival times of ships.

Clue 11

Your next clue can be found in the very back room of the pub.

We've **searched** the sites of bars and restaurants,
for merchants and inhabitants.
Put clues and hints in the frame,
And **laid foundations** of this game.
Tis **days** and **months** that we now seek,
In a print of an old antique.

Eliminate a meeting time

ELIMINATE

If you can't enter the pub, turn to the back page

Story

The day before the launch saw a huge flurry of investment activity regarding Archie's mechanical balloon company; with the stock price fluctuating so much it raised serious suspicions of insider trading.

While huge investment was flooding in, it was also flooding out, and there were some large bets made against the success of the company.

While some put this market fluctuation down to the circulating rumours of financial insecurity and Archie's affair, others suspected that someone knew something about a possible impending disaster or mishap.

Records of these suspicious trades went on to be used in the investigation of Archie's sabotaged balloon.

Directions

Exit The Commercial Rooms and turn left. Head through the row of black bollards and immediately turn right down Exchange Ave. Continue to the end, and when you emerge on St Nicholas St turn left. Turn right just before the church and take the steps down to Baldwin St. After a quick left and right you will be by the river. Head along the cobbled riverside until you reach a domed memorial.

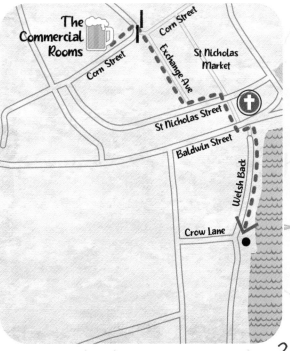

Welsh Back

Bristol's geographical location as an inland port on the River Avon posed several problems for merchants who had to deal with the most variable tide flow in the UK (depth differing up to 40ft) as well as treacherous sailing conditions. In order to face such challenges, ships had to be in excellent, seaworthy condition, and all cargo had to be well packed and stored securely. Herein lies the origin of the expression 'ship-shape and Bristol fashion' to describe something secure, reliable, and in good order.

Clue 12

Look for a dome-shaped monument

3 2

1 4

5 7

'Om.. om'

6

The 4 pictures above represent 4 individual words. Each syllable has been assigned a number. When you match the syllable to the people that the monument is a tribute to, it will form a 4-digit number which is a meeting time to eliminate.

ELIMINATE

Story

The night before the big launch in Queen Square, a local beggar reported seeing a strange transaction take place outside a nearby tavern between a sailor, and a figure concealed in hooded clothing. Details however were very sketchy, and he couldn't remember which tavern it was and what time the transaction took place. What he did say, was that the hooded figure looked extremely nervous and was often looking over his shoulder to see if he was being watched or followed.

The sailor handed him what looked like a large knife or saw, which would be the ideal tool for cutting thick rope found on ships.

Directions

Continue walking south along the river, until you see a large cobblestoned open area on your right (King St). Head through the black bollards and onto this street. On your left you will see the Llandoger Trow, the location of your next clue. (No need to enter).

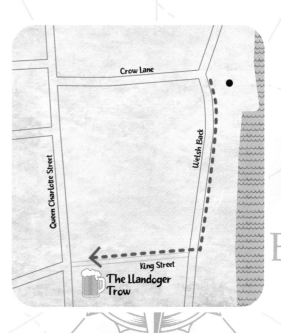

King Street

On the corner of King Street are two legendary Bristol establishments with fascinating history. The Old Duke dates back to 1775, and was originally was called the Duke of Cumberland', named after Prince William Augustus, who gained himself the slur 'Butcher Cumberland' after his bloody and ruthless triumph at the Battle of Culloden. At the famous battle, Cumberland ordered his troops to show 'no mercy', slaughtering the wounded as they lay, and continuing his campaign of terror across the Scottish Highlands long after the battle was over. Across the road is the Llandoger Trow (location of your next clue), which legend has it was the inspiration for the pub featured in Robert Louis Stevenson's Treasure Island, the 'Admiral Benbow Inn'.

Clue 13

Find a plaque on the outside of the pub, and use the missing letters to eliminate a suspect.

Francis Fox

Mortimer Harper

Alex Crest

THE LLANDOGER TROW

TAKES ITS NAME FROM THE TROWS (FLAT _ _ _ _ _ _ _ ED _ _ _ _ _ ING BARGES) WHICH CAME TO THE WELSH BACK

Story

On the day of the flight, security was kept very tight around the balloon as Archie didn't want anyone stealing details of his patented design.

A few very close friends were allowed a quick glimpse of his invention and to wish him luck, but VIPs and press were kept at a safe distance. That meant that very few people had the opportunity to cut a rope without being caught in the act.

As well as the much anticipated air display, a number of stalls provided souvenirs, snacks and drinks, and a pianist was hired to provide musical entertainment for VIP guests. The stage was set for Archie's big moment.

Directions

From The Llandoger Trow head south along Queen Charlotte Street and you will eventually reach a large open area of grass and trees which is Queen Square. The puzzle on the next page leads you to a house number, which is the location of your next clue.

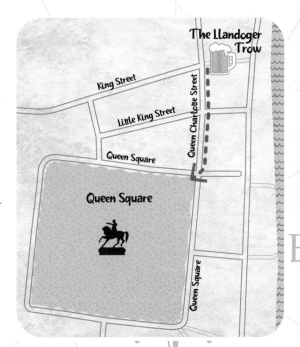

Queen Square

In 1831 this square was the setting for the country's bloodiest domestic riot, with an estimated 500 fatalities and hundreds more wounded. It was the visit of Charles Wetherall which sparked the unrest, who had consistently blocked any attempts at democratic reform, ensuring that only 6,000 people were eligible to vote in the city out of a population of 104,000. Riots lasted for 3 days, and Isambard Kingdom Brunel was even drafted in as a Special Constable to try to keep the peace. Amid the chaos, bullish protestors raised a French Tri-colour flag above the statue of William III in the centre of the square, which struck terror in the government that a French-style revolution may be unfolding on home-soil. Eventually a sword drawn charge was set on the Queen Square protestors, cutting down hundreds in bloody retaliation.

Clue 14

$$\text{horse} + \text{horse} + \text{horse} = 24$$

$$\text{horse} + \text{ships} + \text{ships} = 20$$

(Items placed together should be added)

$$\text{ships} + \text{bottles} + \text{bottle} = 18$$

$$\text{horse} \times \text{bottle} \div \text{ship} = ??$$

Find that house number on Queen Square, and in the centre of the plaster art above the door you will find a tavern to eliminate.

ELIMINATE

31

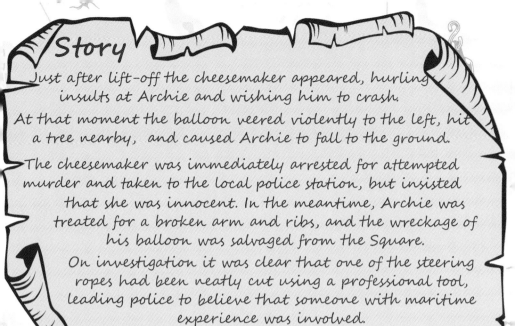

Story

Just after lift-off the cheesemaker appeared, hurling insults at Archie and wishing him to crash.

At that moment the balloon veered violently to the left, hit a tree nearby, and caused Archie to fall to the ground.

The cheesemaker was immediately arrested for attempted murder and taken to the local police station, but insisted that she was innocent. In the meantime, Archie was treated for a broken arm and ribs, and the wreckage of his balloon was salvaged from the Square.

On investigation it was clear that one of the steering ropes had been neatly cut using a professional tool, leading police to believe that someone with maritime experience was involved.

Directions

In the centre of the Square is a statue of William III on horseback. You will notice that one of the horse's hooves is standing on a mound, which famously caused the horse to trip and fatally wound the king.

Head to the north-west corner of the square, and across an open paved area, which leads you to King St. As you emerge from the paved area, you will notice a gated area of pink buildings, which is the location of your next clue

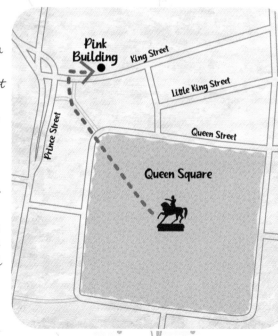

32

Merchant Almshouses

The pink buildings in front of you are a perfect representation of the difficult relationship between Bristol's development, and its link to the slave trade. Built in 1696 by the Bristol Society of Merchant Venturers, these houses were built to provide care for sailors who had fallen ill or lost their eyesight due to the effects of fever caught while serving on slave ships. Whilst the Society funded a wide variety of beneficial projects to the city, including Clifton Suspension Bridge, Great Western Railway and Bristol's floating harbour, they were also the driving force who lobbied parliament to open up the slave trade in 1698, from which most of their profits derived. By the 18th century, a quarter of all their members were involved in the slave trade, including Edward Colston, who famously had his statue torn down 2020.

Clue 15

Freed from all storms 666 tem5555 and the rage
44 billows, here we spend our 777.
Our weather beaten vessels here re3333
And from the Merchants' kind and generous care
1111 harbour here; no more we put to sea
Until we launch into Eternity.
And lest our Widows whom we leave behind
Should want relief, they too 2 shelter find.
Thus all our anxious cares and sorrows cease
Whilst our kind Guardians turn our toils to ease.
May they be with an endless Sabbath blest
Who have afforded unto us this rest.

Find this wording on the outside of the Almshouse, and enter the missing words in order below:

__1__   _2_   __3__   _4_   ___5___(s) (on) _6_ (front) p__7_

Eliminate a business

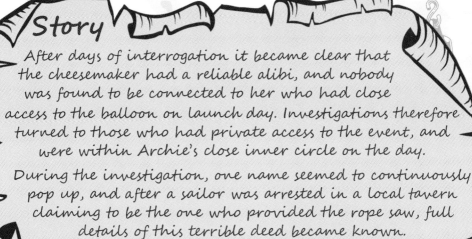

Story

After days of interrogation it became clear that the cheesemaker had a reliable alibi, and nobody was found to be connected to her who had close access to the balloon on launch day. Investigations therefore turned to those who had private access to the event, and were within Archie's close inner circle on the day.

During the investigation, one name seemed to continuously pop up, and after a sailor was arrested in a local tavern claiming to be the one who provided the rope saw, full details of this terrible deed became known.

Archie continued to recover from the broken arm and ribs he suffered after falling from the balloon, but would find it emotionally hard to recover after learning of his friend's betrayal.

Directions

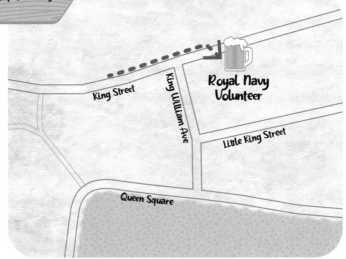

King Street

King William Ave

Royal Navy Volunteer

Little King Street

Queen Square

Keep the Almshouses on your left, and continue along King Street until you see the Royal Navy Volunteer pub on your right-hand side, which is your final stop.

Royal Navy Volunteer

In the 18th century, Britain was almost always at war, which created a constant need for the fresh supply of able men who were often forced into service by the infamous 'Press Gang'. Several pubs in this area would help protect their regular drinkers against the threat of these roaming thugs, including The Hole in the Wall (near Queen Square), which still has original lookout holes built into its walls. It is unknown how many were recruited in the city, as when a man was captured he would often sign up as a recruit rather than a pressed sailor in order to be eligible for a split of prize money and a sign-up bonus. In 1787 one man was hanged for signing up to serve in the Navy, receiving his bonus, then disappearing, and repeating this act 47 times.

Clue 16

Four sailors arrested in this pub for drunken behaviour claimed to have overheard the meeting between the guilty parties, and could finally shed light on the mystery...

Philip igram

Eric atler

David ogre

Thor sedgewick

Potential suspects and lists of names seem to last forever, whilst it could be the <u>end of one, it links you to another</u>.

(You don't need to find anything at the location to solve this clue)

Eliminate your final suspect

ELIMINATE

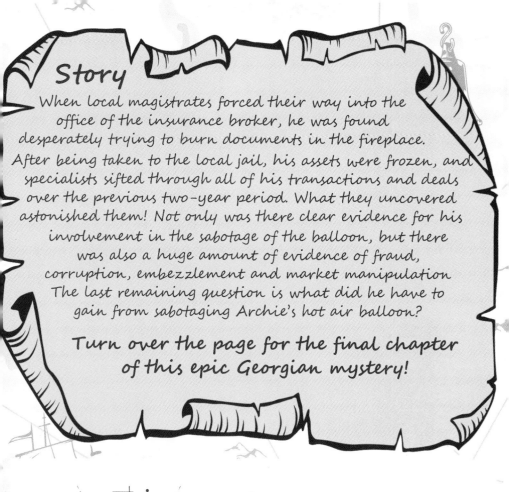

Story

When local magistrates forced their way into the office of the insurance broker, he was found desperately trying to burn documents in the fireplace. After being taken to the local jail, his assets were frozen, and specialists sifted through all of his transactions and deals over the previous two-year period. What they uncovered astonished them! Not only was there clear evidence for his involvement in the sabotage of the balloon, but there was also a huge amount of evidence of fraud, corruption, embezzlement and market manipulation The last remaining question is what did he have to gain from sabotaging Archie's hot air balloon?

Turn over the page for the final chapter of this epic Georgian mystery!

Congratulations

You have solved all of the clues and completed the mystery! However one question remains:

Why was the balloon sabotaged?

The final chapter...

The investigation into Mortimer Harper's accounts showed that his motives for sabotaging Archie's balloon were two-fold. The first reason was simple; he had been behind many huge bets against the company the day before the event, knowing that the stock price would plummet. The second reason shocked the city of Bristol and resulted in a 25-year jail sentence for the disgraced trader. Over the past five years, Mortimer Harper had been sponsoring attacks on coaches and paying highwaymen to spread fear and chaos in the roads around the city in order to drive up insurance premiums and make him rich. Harper felt that flight-based travel could be the future, and believed that if Archie's balloon was to crash in front of investors, this too could drive up the price of insurance in the industry. Along with a jail sentence, Harper's assets were seized and handed over to the city to be used in making Bristol 'The Ballooning Capital of Britain'. A dedicated research centre was opened in Clifton, and an annual event was staged. Archie finally got his wish, and took to the skies in his repaired balloon along with his loving family and the finest bottle of French champagne in tribute to the Montgolfier brothers, whose original invention had inspired him to dedicate his life to the art of the hot air balloon!